The Apothecary
in Eighteenth-Century Williamsburg

O F THE FIRST 225 men sent over from London to settle at Jamestown in 1607 and 1608, seven were practitioners of medicine —as it was then practiced: Walter Russell, Gent., was a "Doctour of Physicke," which is to say that he had studied at a university and earned a degree in medicine; Thomas Wotton, Will Wilkinson, and Post Ginnat were listed as surgeons—"chirurgeon" as it then appeared; Thomas Field and John Harford bore the label of apothecaries; and the seventh was "Tho: Cowper the Barber."

Plainly, the Virginia Company of London, numbering several prominent medical men among its backers, wanted its adventurers to the New World to have the best of medical care. Unfortunately for about four of every five settlers in the first few years at Jamestown, the best was not enough to avert wholesale mortality from sickness, Indian arrows, and "meere famine." That some of the medical men shared the fate of their patients seems likely in the absence of later information about most of them.

Medical theories and practices at the beginning of the seventeenth century were largely those that had prevailed since the time of Galen, a Greek physician who died about two centuries after Christ. According to Galen, the four elements of Aristotelian science—fire, water, air, and earth—comprised the four major humors of the human body: blood, phlegm, yellow bile, and black bile. Blood was held to be moist and warm, phlegm was moist and cool, yellow bile dry and warm, and black bile dry and cold.

Sickness, in the theory of Galen, was caused by one or more of these humors becoming impure or out of place or out of balance. Treatment thus consisted of removing or diminishing the offending humor by purging, bleeding, vomiting, blistering, urinating, sweating, or salivating; on the other hand, a deficient humor was to be restored by diet and drugs. Galen classed drugs according to their warm, cold, moist, or dry qualities. For instance, pepper was a heating drug, good for chills, while cucumber was a cool one, to be given in case of fever.

Galenism had been subjected to attack in the sixteenth century by Paracelsus and Vesalius, but its appeal was logical and remained strong in seventeenth-century England. (In fact, some survivals can be found in twentieth-century folk medicine.) Dr. Lawrence Bohun (or Boone), who came over in 1610 and returned to England in 1611, spent some of the year investigating medicinal sources in Virginia. He discovered a white clay—and shipped some to England— that he claimed could absorb and expel poisons from the body. Among vegetable remedies, Bohun experimented with sassafras and found *"Galbanum mechoacon*, otherwise called *rubarbum alum*, to be of service in cold moist bodies, for the purginge of fleame [phlegm] and superfluous matter."

WHAT IS AN APOTHECARY?

Already it will be evident that the practice of medicine in seventeenth-century England, and hence in the first American colonies, was not neatly confined to the licensed graduates of accredited medical schools. Quite the contrary. In fact, Henry VIII had complained that all kinds of ignorant people got into the act, including "Smiths, Weavers, and Women."

The Doctors' Dispensatory.
or the Art of Phisick restored to practice.

The Apothecary's Shop opened.

Sold by N: Brooke at ŷ Angell in Cornhill.

In the upper half of this woodcut from **The Expert Doctor's Dispensary,** *published in* **London in 1657,** *a learned physician is shown conducting a urinalysis. He simply holds the flask of liquid to the light for visual examination. Below, a customer presents what appears to be a written prescription to be filled by the apothecary.*

Two centuries of legal and parliamentary pulling and hauling, plus the consequence of some natural developments, left the situation in England somewhat stabilized—but not necessarily logical. The barbers, chartered as a guild in 1462 and authorized to practice surgery, included both barbers and surgeons in growing disharmony until they were formally divorced in 1745.

The apothecaries—the word originally meant shopkeeper—joined the guild of grocers at one time but shortly broke away to form their own guild in 1617. Meantime, the physicians, organized in the College of Physicians, obtained the right to keep watch on the apothecaries.

Physicians, who had to have as much as 14 years training and four degrees from Oxford or Cambridge, were naturally not abundant. Being learned men, they would not stoop to the indignity of such menial work as performing surgical operations or compounding medicines. The former was the province of the surgeon or barber-surgeon, the latter was the specialty of the apothecary.

But the scarcity of physicians, especially in rural areas, left a medical gap that the apothecaries, trained through apprenticeship and many times more numerous, naturally moved to fill. In 1727 English law finally recognized and legalized the fact that for most people the apothecary-surgeon was the only available practitioner of medicine. In turn, the business of purveying drugs and compounding medicines passed from the apothecaries to the wholesale druggists and pharmaceutical chemists.

As it was transferred to America the trade of apothecary—it was neither a craft nor a profession in any strict sense—was probably much like that of the rural apothecary-surgeon of seventeenth-century England. The apothecary still made his living primarily from the provision of drugs and medical preparations; but he also performed amputations, dressed wounds, and subjected his patients to the normal medical treatments of the day.

ALL THAT THE LAW ALLOWS

Virginia was the only colony that tried to draw legislative boundaries around the various aspects of medical practice. The effort came in 1736 in the form of "an Act for Regulating the Fees and Accounts of the Practicers of Phisic." On two grounds the act deserves to be quoted at some length. For one thing, it throws a good light on the state of medical practice at that time. For another, it affords

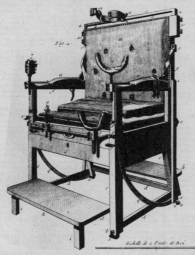

An eighteenth-century operating chair, fully equipped with tilting back, padded adjustable supports, and straps to keep the patient from writhing away from the knife. Anesthesia was limited to strong doses of spirituous liquors; antisepsis was unknown. The illustration is taken from Denis Diderot's famous encyclopedia of arts and sciences.

undeniable parallels to some current problems in the cost of medicines and medical care, and to the role of government in serving the interests of the "consumer."

The first section of the act recited certain abuses, especially of the surgeons and apothecaries:

I. Whereas the practice of phisic in this colony, is most commonly taken up and followed, by surgeons, apothecaries, or such as have only served apprenticeships to those trades, who often prove very unskilful in the art of a phisician; and yet do demand excessive fees, and exact unreasonable prices for the medicines which they

administer, and do too often, for the sake of making
up long and expensive bills, load their patients with
greater quantities thereof, than are necessary or useful,
concealing all their compositions, as well to prevent the
discovery of their practice, as of the true value of what
they administer: which is become a grievance, dangerous
and intolerable, as well to the poorer sort of people as
others, & doth require the most effectual remedy that
the nature of the thing will admit.

The second section then proceeded to emphasize the
chief distinction between the apprentice-trained apothecary-
surgeons and the university-educated physicians by allow-
ing the latter to charge twice as much for their services
as the former could. If the apothecaries and surgeons
felt—as well they might have—that the difference in fees
was an insult to them, it did not last long. The law was
not renewed at the following session of the Assembly;
perhaps its backers, the physicians, had seen their
patients flock to the lower-priced practicers.

Although Virginia was the only colony to set medical
fees by law, the practice of legislative price fixing in other
areas of the economy was as common in colonial America as
it was in England. In Virginia, to be specific, not only
prices and quantities but in some cases even qualities
of goods and services offered to the public by tavernkeepers,
shoemakers, millers, and ferrymen were regulated by law.
The economic philosophy and terminology of *laissez faire*
were among the alien isms imported after 1776. During
the colonial years, government rarely hesitated to act in
the economic field where the need was felt.

From this particular Virginia law of 1736 it would appear
that some if not all medical charges had gotten well out
of line—the correct line, of course, being what the people
and their elected representatives thought was reasonable:

II. BE it therefore enacted, . . .
     That from and after the passing of this
     act, no practicer in phisic, in any action or

suit whatsoever, hereafter to be commenced in any court of record in this colony, shall recover, for visiting any sick person, more than the rates hereafter mentioned: that is to say,

Surgeons and apothecaries, who have served an apprenticeship to those trades, shall be allowed,

	£	s	d
For every visit, and prescription, in town, or within five miles	oo	5	oo
For every mile, above five, and under ten	oo	1	oo
For a visit, of ten miles	oo	10	oo
And for every mile, above ten	oo	oo	o6
With an allowance for all ferriages in their journeys.			
To Surgeons, For a simple fracture, and the cure thereof	o2	oo	oo
For a compound fracture, and the cure thereof	o4	oo	oo

But those persons who have studied phisic in any university, and taken any degree therein, shall be allowed,

	£	s	d
For every visit, and prescription, in any town, or within five miles	oo	10	oo
If above five miles, for every mile more, under ten	oo	1	oo
For a visit, if not above ten miles	1	oo	oo
And for every mile, above ten	oo	1	oo

With an allowance of ferriages, as before.

Lest it appear that all Williamsburg "practicers" made a habit of charging excessive fees, the generous treatment an earlier doctor gave at least one of his patients must be set down. George Hume, a Scottish merchant who came to Virginia about 1722 and soon caught all the prevalent ills, found the place "only good for doctors and ministers who have very good encouragem'nt here." One of the "common distempers" that afflicted Hume was dysentery, then called the flux. He was laid so low that Dr.

John Brown all but despaired of his life. Hume's gratitude for being cured was doubtless enhanced by the fact—carefully reported to his Scottish relatives—that "ye Dr. took nothing for my druggs."

The third section of the act, specifying exactly what the "practicer of phisic" should set forth in his bill, bears at least a faint augury of modern food-and-drug labeling legislation:

> III. And to the end the true value of the medicines administered by any practicer in phisic, may be better known, and judged of, *Be it further enacted, by the authority aforesaid,* That whenever any pills, bolus, portion, draught, electuary, decoction, or any medicines, in any form whatsoever, shall be administered to any sick person, the person administering the same shall, at the same time, deliver in his bill, expressing every particular thing made up therein; or if the medicine administered, be a simple, or compound, directed in the *dispensatories*, the true name thereof shall be expressed in the same bill, together with the quantities and prices, in both cases. And in failure thereof, such practicer, or any apothecary, making up the prescription of another, shall be nonsuited, in any action or suit hereafter commenced, which shall be grounded upon such bill or bills: Nor shall any book, or account, of any practicer in phisic, or any apothecary, be permitted to be given in evidence, before a court; unless the articles therein contained, be charged according to the directions of this act.

This final section reveals that some differentiation between the branches of the medical profession had already begun in America. The tip-off is the phrase that imposes on "any apothecary making up the prescription of another" the same requirements as on physicians who make up their own prescriptions.

THE DOCTORS OF WILLIAMSBURG

If competition tends to keep prices low, fees charged in and around the capital city in the early eighteenth century

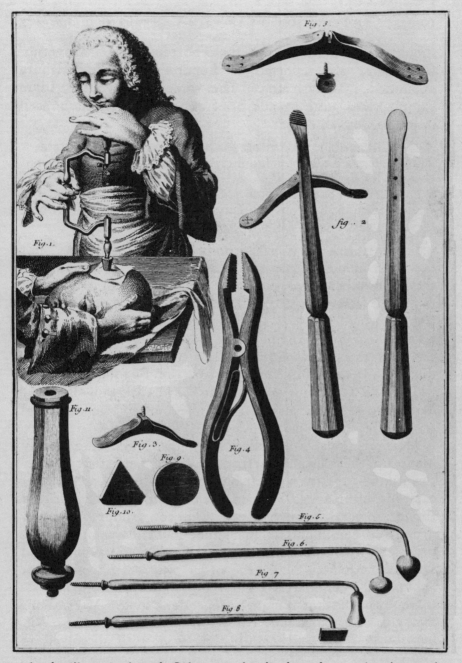

Another illustration from the Diderot encyclopedia shows the operation of trepanning a skull and some surgical tools in common use in the eighteenth century, in colonial America as well as in Europe.

should have been at the rock bottom level. Governor
Gooch in 1729 reported to London that Williamsburg
abounded in physicians. The same year young Adam
Cunningham gave up his brief effort to establish himself
in practice as a doctor:

> Williamsburg [he wrote] is but a small Village contain-
> ing not more than 60 families, at most; and in and about
> this City are no less than 25 or 30 phisitians, and of that
> number not above 2 capable of living handsomly. So that I
> did not think it proper to stay, in a place where so many
> of my profession are lickely to starve.

Little is known about any of these "phisitians," not
even the names of most. It seems fairly sure, however,
that a number were quacks. Gooch had complained in
the same letter about the "unskilfulness of practioners in
this country" but was gullible enough himself to pay 60
pounds from public funds and give freedom to a Negro
slave for the secret of the latter's alleged cure of venereal
diseases. It turned out to be a decoction of roots and barks,
which the Governor avowed to be "a certain Remedy
here" and sent samples so the College of Physicians could
try its effect in England.

Most of Gooch's abundant physicians almost certainly
made up their own prescriptions. From 1622 at Jamestown until 1731 in Williamsburg no mention of an apothecary in Virginia has been found in historical records. In
the latter year, however, there were four shops purveying
drugs and compounding medicines in Williamsburg. The
proprietors of two were doctors—Dr. George Gilmer and
Dr. Kenneth McKenzie; the other two were druggists or
"chymists"—Thomas Wharton and Thomas Goodwin.

Goodwin did not remain independent long. After about
two years he joined Dr. Robert Davidson, mayor of Williamsburg, in a partnership that was itself dissolved in
two years by the death of Dr. Davidson. Thomas Wharton,
on the other hand, kept shop in Williamsburg for some
eleven years. He had arrived in Virginia about 1703 as an

indentured servant to a Dr. Richard Wright and had acquired by the time of his death in 1746 not only a pharmaceutical business, but the title of "Doctor." He willed his drugs, medicines, and shop utensils to Dr. McKenzie.

SHOPKEEPER EXTRAORDINARY

The fourth named practicer, George Gilmer, Sr., deserves extended attention. He comes as close as any one person to being a typical Williamsburg apothecary-surgeon-physician of his time, though his extramedical career was far from typical.

Born in Edinburgh in 1700, Gilmer studied medicine there, then practiced with one of London's leading doctors, whose daughter he married. Possibly the death of his young wife moved him to ship for America; at the age of 31 he arrived in Virginia to practice medicine and manage the affairs of a land company. He married again and must have prospered, because in four years' time he was able to purchase for £155 three choice lots near the Governor's Palace in Williamsburg.

These three lots, on which the rambling St. George Tucker House has stood since 1788, were described in 1735 as "the Lotts and Land whereon the Bowling Green formerly was, the Dwelling House and Kitchen of William Levingston and the House call'd the Play House." The last, of course, was the first theater in the English colonies, and Gilmer later sold it to the mayor and aldermen of Williamsburg to be used as a city hall and courthouse. It was a particularly convenient arrangement for one of the aldermen who was to become mayor himself a year later, none other than Dr. George Gilmer.

Gilmer's career as an apothecary-surgeon-physician was not without its ups and downs. Soon after buying the property on Palace Green, he was giving away samples of rattlesnake root on behalf of Dr. John Tennent, who maintained it would cure pleurisy, the gout, rheumatism, and mad-dog bites.

At the same time the *Virginia Gazette*, Williamsburg's new weekly, carried the news that "on *Monday* Morning last, dy'd, at Mr. *Geo. Gilmer's*, in this City, Mrs. *Susanna Skaife*, . . . and was decently interr'd on *Wensday*. And, on *Thursday* Morning also dy'd, the Rev. Mr. *John Skaife*, her Husband, after a tedious Indisposition." It would appear that at least Mrs. Skaife was a bed patient in Dr. Gilmer's

Surrounded by the equipment of his craft, this young apothecary is making up a prescription of some kind, probably for pills. The illustration traces back to a London publication, The Book of Trades or Library of Useful Arts, *first American edition published in 1807 by J. Johnson and for sale in his bookstore in Philadelphia and in Richmond, Virginia.*

home; this was a usual way of caring for serious illnesses before the day of hospitals.

Soon thereafter, Gilmer found it necessary to insert the following advertisement in the *Virginia Gazette*:

Williamsburg *May* 26, 1737.
There *being a Report industriously spread about the Country, of* George Gilmer's *Death, by some well-meaning*

People, and of his being so much in Debt, that nothing from
England *would be sent him this Year*, if alive.

To obviate such scandalous and groundless Reports, *I
take this Opportunity to acquaint all my Friends, that I can
now, better than ever, supply them with all manner of
Chymical and Galenical Medicines, truly and faithfully prepared, and at as cheap Rates as can be had from* England.
*Also Double-refin'd, Single refin'd, and Lump Sugars, Cin-
namon, Cloves, Mace, Nutmegs,* Bateman's *Drops,* Squire's
Elixir, Anderson's *Pills, Sweet Oil, &c. at reasonable Rates;
at my Old Shop, near the* Governor's.

George Gilmer

Nine years later Gilmer was so much alive and active
as to be mayor of the city, the owner of a new four-wheeled
chaise, and once more a bridegroom. On the death of
his second wife, Gilmer had promptly married his next-
door neighbor. The third Mrs. Gilmer was Harrison
Blair, daughter of Dr. Archibald Blair and sister of the
Hon. John Blair of the governor's council. The apothecary's star was rising.

He was still, of course, a shopkeeper. His "Old Shop
near the Governor's" stood at the very edge of Palace
Green, a frame building of about 20 feet square. Every
year or so he advertised the arrival from England of a
shipment of drugs, medicines, spices, and groceries—to be
sold at the shop, wholesale or retail, and at reasonable rates.

Archaeological excavations on the site of the first theater,
and extending north of it onto the adjacent Brush-Everard
House property, yielded quantities of Dr. Gilmer's domestic and pharmaceutical rubbish. The latter included delft-
ware ointment pots and drug jars, glass medicine phials
and fragments of carboys, bottles for Pyrmont mineral
water, a brass pestle, and, inexplicably, a human jaw. Just
how, or if, that related to Gilmer's shop remains open to
conjecture, but it is evident from the quantity of pharmaceutical artifacts recovered that Dr. Gilmer's business was
as extensive as his 1737 advertisement claimed.

Indeed, Gilmer was no ordinary shopkeeper. His social status—doubtless bolstered by that of his wife's family—was great enough that he could be among the first to entertain the newly appointed Governor Dinwiddie. One suspects that either the ambitious Dr. Gilmer or his well-born wife decided that his house on Palace Street fell short of such prestigious demands. Six months after the dinner for Dinwiddie, the apothecary was having his dining room wainscoted, with a marble fireplace, a mirror over the mantel, and a cabinet to contain the set of new china his wife had ordered from London.

About the same time Dr. Gilmer, who gave himself perhaps facetiously the title of "colonel," became part owner of the Raleigh Tavern. The deed by which he and Colonel Chiswell bought the famous inn for £700 testified that he had gained that ultimate accolade of social and economic status in colonial Virginia, the designation "Geo Gilmer Gent."

In the letters he wrote to London, Gilmer seems to refer to himself not as a doctor or surgeon, but as an apothecary, and his name in public documents as well as in private records most often appears not as Dr. Gilmer but as Mr. Gilmer. He was doubtless prouder of being known as a gentleman and a colonel; the title of doctor was often held in poor esteem. William Byrd II wrote in 1706 that "here be some men indeed that are call'd Doctors: but they are generally discarded Surgeons of Ships, that know nothing above the very common Remedys." As late as 1783 Dr. Johann Schoepf, writing of his travels through the former colonies, asserted that "in America every man who drives the curing trade is known without distinction as Doctor, as elsewhere every person who makes verses is a poet—so there are both black doctors and brown, and quacks in abundance."

THE EDUCATION OF AN APOTHECARY

Apprenticeship was the usual form of training for all

colonial occupations, with the possible exception of the ministry at one end of the scale and ordinary farming at the other. Medicine was not an exception; practitioners normally took apprentices for the same reasons that cabinet-makers or blacksmiths did. The beginning apprentice performed the unskilled and some of the semiskilled duties of the establishment, learning as he did so. As he acquired knowledge, he could give the doctor more and more assistance in his practice.

The doctor generally undertook, if there was a formal indenture, to teach the apprentice the "art and mystery of physic, surgery, and pharmacy," or words to that effect. Sometimes, however, he agreed to teach only the art of the apothecary. In either event, the apprentice was taught to compound medicines as directed by his master, to search the woods for medicinal plants, and probably to keep books and collect fees. Even an apprentice apothecary might in time be called on to assist—or perhaps even take over—such routine treatments as bleeding. Most likely he also had to spend his evenings reading whatever medical or pharmaceutical works the doctor had on hand—from Hippocrates to the latest edition of the *Edinburgh Pharmacopoeia.*

On completing this apprenticeship—which in most cases probably fell short of the English norm of seven years—the young man could set up in the "curing trade" for himself, with no more credentials than his master's certificate to the effect that he had served a certain term and had studied certain books. Or he could go to Edinburgh or London for further study at a university or in a hospital.

In any event, there was no requirement that a dealer in drugs or a practicer of medicine must have a degree, a license, or any other recommendation than his own assurance of good results to the sick who applied to him. Some practitioners were on the modest side in offering their services; some were wholly unrestrained—even guaranteeing to cure cancer! The contrast stands out sharply in these

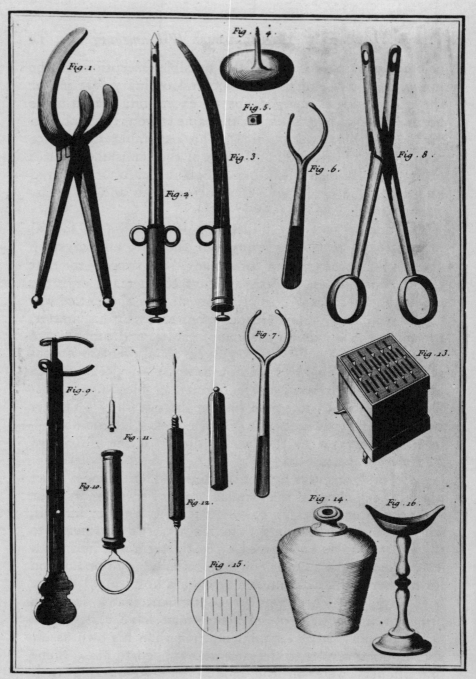

Fig. 1.
Fig. 2.
Fig. 3.
Fig. 4.
Fig. 5.
Fig. 6.
Fig. 7.
Fig. 8.
Fig. 9.
Fig. 10.
Fig. 11.
Fig. 12.
Fig. 13.
Fig. 14.
Fig. 15.
Fig. 16.

Another plate from Diderot's encyclopedia shows a variety of instruments used by eighteenth-century apothecary-surgeons. Notice the box-like device with 16 small knives that can be pressed against the skin and triggered to make simultaneous incisions for bleeding a patient. One of these gadgets can be seen at the Apothecary Shop in Williamsburg.

two advertisements from the *Virginia Gazette*, the first
in 1771 by Dr. William Stark of the town of Blandford,
the second five years later by a quack who did not even
bother to give himself the title of doctor.

> The Subscriber having been bred to Physick in his
> younger Years, and having attended particularly to this
> Study for these three Years past, now proposes to practise
> on the most moderate Terms. He cannot with Sincerity
> boast of having attained the *Ne plus ultra* of the *Aesculapian*
> Art, nor yet of acquiring any superior Degree of Knowl-
> edge in this Science; but flatters himself that, by a vigilant
> and due Attention to the Indications and Efforts of Nature
> in those sick Persons who should, through Choice or Neces-
> sity, be committed to his Care, he may be able to afford
> them proper and timely Assistance.

* * *

> Thomas Johnson, of Brunswick, Who is well known for
> his Abilities in the Cure of the Flux, gives Notice that he
> also cures the following Disorders, *viz.* the Spleen, Cholic,
> Asthma, and any Kind of Fevers, lingering Disorders, bad
> Coughs, Scurvy, any Kind of running Humours or scorbutic
> Disorders, the Yaws and *French* Disorder, without Saliva-
> tion, sore Legs, Dropsy, Scurvy in the Gums, and has the
> greatest Reason to believe he can cure the Consumption if
> timely applied to.

LINES OF SUCCESSION

In a very direct and personal way, each generation
of Williamsburg physician-apothecary trained its successor.
Two particularly illustrative lines began with Dr. George
Gilmer.

At one time in 1745 it appears that Gilmer had an
apprentice by the name of James Carter. A few years
later Carter opened an apothecary shop of his own at the
sign of the Unicorn's Horn, next door to the Raleigh
Tavern in Williamsburg. Carter in turn took Andrew
Anderson as apprentice, and in due time, when Anderson
had attained the status of "doctor," took him into partner-

ship. This combination lasted only two years, and James Carter later formed a partnership with his brother William, a physician. After another few years James sold his share of the apothecary shop to William but apparently continued independently to practice medicine until his death in 1794.

Gilmer, of course, had long since taken another apprentice in young James Carter's place. Billy Pasteur was the son of the barber and wigmaker, who could not afford to send his son abroad for medical study. But at the end of his apprenticeship, Pasteur did go to London with the help of Dr. Gilmer for a year's study at St. Thomas's Hospital. He returned to Williamsburg and opened shop just after his benefactor's death. It would seem probable that he took over Gilmer's shop before building his own, though the record does not say.

Pasteur, in his own turn, had at least two apprentices who later practiced in Williamsburg. The second, Robert Nicolson, shortly moved his apothecary shop and medical practice to Yorktown, thereby taking himself out of this narrative. His predecessor, John Minson Galt, remained in Williamsburg and in the medical profession until 1808. Like Dr. Gilmer, who educated his own son, George Gilmer, Jr., in medicine, John Minson Galt launched two of his sons into medicine via apprenticeship.

A son of Samuel Galt, the silversmith, John Minson Galt was apprenticed at the age of 14 to William Pasteur, who himself had just set up shop and was only half a dozen years older. The apprenticeship appears to have lasted a full term of seven years. It was followed by two years of medicine in London. There the young man studied the theory and practice of physic under Dr. Hugh Smith, midwifery under Dr. Colin McKenzie, and surgery, anatomy, and operations at St. Thomas's Hospital. Galt is also said to have attended the College of William and Mary—presumably before going abroad—and to have pursued his medical studies in Edinburgh and Paris as well as in London. All of this made John Minson Galt undoubtedly the best educated apothecary-surgeon of eighteenth-century Williamsburg.

On his return to Williamsburg in 1769 he bought "a box of Surgeon's Instruments," married Judith Craig, and announced his intention to open shop at "the Brick House, opposite the Coffee House when he gets his utensils fixed." The *Virginia Gazette*'s notice of the marriage was short and full of confident optimism:

> This evening Doctor JOHN MINSON GALT, of this city, was married to Miss JUDITH CRAIG, eldest daughter of Mr. ALEXANDER CRAIG. The mutual affection and familiarity of disposition in this agreeable pair, afford the strongest assurance of their enjoying the highest felicity in the nuptial state.

In setting up shop as an apothecary-surgeon in Williamsburg, Galt was not exactly filling a vacuum. In fact, the same issue of the *Gazette* in which he announced himself carried long advertisements by two other apothecaries. One was Galt's former master and benefactor, William Pasteur; the other was "Andrew Anderson, Surgeon and Man-Midwife," also just launching in practice. Altogether the ads occupy a little over one whole column of the paper, and each consists almost solely of a list of the items available at that shop.

It is interesting to notice that William Pasteur had imported a new supply of goods in the same ship with Galt's "compleat assortment," and just in time:

> The subscriber having had but very few medicines left in his shop before this order came to hand, will now be able to furnish his friends and customers with every thing fresh and genuine. Gentlemen practitioners, and others, may depend on being supplied at a very low advance.

The final assurance echoes Pasteur's earlier complaint written his London agents to the effect that "tiss hardly worth our while to import medicines for sale we are Oblige to sell at a low advance on acc^t of our confounded druggist here. . . ." The "confounded druggist," William Biers, was having his own difficulties making a living, however, and soon sold out to the partnership of James Carter and Andrew Anderson.

Colonial Williamsburg owns several of Dr. Galt's account books, including the one for the years 1770 to 1775, before he joined Pasteur. One of the early entries shows a charge against Thomas Glass of ten shillings for "visiting &c." The corresponding credit entry shows that the bill was paid in cash seven years and five months later! Patients were as lax about paying their doctor's bills then as now, and although most of Dr. Galt's patients paid in cash, he also took wood, hay, and oats. On one instance he wrote off a debt with an equal credit "for the Runaway."

What is surely the most provocative entry occurs opposite February 29, 1772, a Leap Year Day. On that date appears a debit against a Mr. Bowyer of 10 shillings for "attend^{ce} in the night." On the credit side are these words in Galt's hand: "Twas sewed on by a Girl who I shou'd be happy with." Does this mean that in three short years the "mutual affection and familiarity of disposition" of John and Judith had worn away? The account book does not answer.

Notice that Galt's charge of 10 shillings for visiting a patient was the very sum permitted by law in 1736—three and a half decades earlier. For amputating Mr. Parson's finger and dressing it he charged £3 4s 6d, and the same amount to Mr. Cardwell for "laying open Child's leg &c."

There is but a single entry for bleeding, and in this case the patient was a Negro. Dr. Galt, unlike most of his colleagues, seems not to have favored phlebotomy. The great number of entries simply mention visiting, attendance, or advice, with prescriptions by the score of cathartics, emetics, purges, etc.

PASTEUR & GALT

It must have been a source of gratification to John

Minson Galt when the well-established Pasteur invited the younger man to become his partner.   The announce- of the new firm read as follows:

WILLIAMSBURG, *April* 15, 1775

THE Subscribers having this Day entered into Partnership, beg Leave to acquaint the Public in general, and their Friends and Neighbours in particular, that they intend practicing Physic and Surgery to their fullest Extent; and that they intend also, as soon as the Situation of the Times will admit, to keep full and complete Assortments of Drugs and Medicines, which they will endeavour to procure of the very best in Quality, and will take Care to have them fresh by making several Importations in the Year. It is proposed that *John M. Galt* shall pay his particular Attention to Surgery, to whom our Friends are desired to apply on all such occasions, but will be advised and assisted by *W. Pasteur* in all difficult Cases. They both desire to make their most grateful Acknowledgments to their Friends and Cus- tomers for the many Favours and Civilities they have re- ceived, and hope, by this Union, they will be enabled to carry on their Business to the entire Satisfaction of their Friends; as, on their Part, the strictest Assiduity and At- tention shall be observed.

PASTEUR & GALT

Only a few days after this announcement appeared, the spark of revolution flared out in both Lexington, Mas- sachusetts, and Williamsburg, Virginia.   As it happened, Dr. Pasteur was to play a minor role and a momentary one on the Williamsburg stage.   Governor Dunmore's sur- reptitious removal of the colony's gunpowder from the Magazine was detected and there was an immediate reaction from the populace, some under arms.   Attending a patient in the Palace, Dr. Pasteur was twice accosted by the Governor and made the bearer of angry messages to the Speaker of the House of Burgesses and "the Gentlemen of the Town."   Should he be attacked, His Lordship blus- tered, "he would declare freedom to the slaves & reduce the city of Williamsburg to ashes."

What actually followed was that Dunmore and his family fled the Palace, never to return, and Pasteur became the next mayor of Williamsburg. It should be mentioned that he and John Minson Galt were already members of the Committee of Safety for the city when they formed their partnership. The sympathies of both were clearly on the patriot side.

The partners very shortly were able to advertise the importation of the usual wide assortment of drugs and medicines for sale in their shop on Duke of Gloucester Street. And a few surviving bills indicate that they did not lack for medical and surgical business. Dr. Pasteur, it would seem, did not share his younger colleague's aversion to phlebotomy, as the following excerpt from a Pasteur & Galt bill to Henry Morse Esq. in 1775 shows:

April	14	To bleeding Vomit & Chamomile Flowers	. . 7	. . 6	
	21	To Brimstone & Antimony	. . 1	. . 3	
	22	To Purge Honey & Barley	. . 4	. .	
	25	To Purge 2/6. 26 Sugar Candy 1/3	. . 3	. . 9	
	29	To bleeding & Pectoral Mixture	. . 8	. . 6	
	30	To Visiting Mixture & Sago	. . 9	. . 9	
May	4	To Pectoral Mixture	. . 6	. . 6	
	11	To 1 lb Balsam Honey	. . 6	. . 3	
	19	To 1 lb Do. 6/3 25 Honey 1/0 31*st* Cons. Roses 2/	. . 9	. . 3	
June	1	To 1 lb Balsam Honey	. . 6	. . 3	
	6	To Lenitive Electary & Salope	. . 3	. . 6	
	15	To Castor Oil & Honey	. . 6	. .	
	16	To Febrifuge & Bitter Decoctions	. .12	. .	
	22	To Attend*ce* & Bleedg in the Night	. .10	. .	
	23	To Honey & Oxymel Squills	. . 2	. . 6	
July	10	To Honey 1/ 10*th* Capillaire & Sago 5/6	. . 6	. . 6	
August	20	To Vomit & Chamomile Flowers	. . 2	. . 6	
	21	To Febrifuge Decoction repeated	. .10	. .	

L 5. 16 . 6

The partnership lasted only three years, for reasons

not now discernable, and William Pasteur gave notice to the public that "I purpose commencing oyster merchant" at his landing on King's Creek between Williamsburg and Yorktown. Galt, on the other hand, continued to practice medicine, serving as a senior surgeon to the Continental military hospital in Williamsburg, joining in partnership with Dr. Philip Barraud, and becoming visiting physician to the public hospital for the insane and a member of its board of directors. He held both offices until his death in 1808. Yet as late as 1794 he was identified in court records as "Apothecary, of the City of Williamsburg."

THE APOTHECARY SHOP

The Pasteur-Galt apothecary shop on Duke of Gloucester Street in Williamsburg is a reconstruction. Its size and location are determined with certainty not only from an eighteenth-century town map, but also by eighteenth-century foundations excavated on the site. The land was owned by Dr. William Pasteur from 1760 until 1778, during which time he probably built the shop. When he and John Minson Galt dissolved their partnership, he sold the property to Galt, who transferred it to his son at the end of the century.

No record survives as to the exact appearance, outside or inside, of the Pasteur-Galt shop. Some apothecary shops apparently had as many as three rooms: the front shop, the doctor's office and operating room, and possibly a sort of laboratory where the apprentice compounded medicines. The Pasteur-Galt shop has been reconstructed with two, the preparative work being done in full view of the public.

As to the content of the shop, ample evidence comes from almost any advertisement of Galt, Pasteur, or for that matter of just about any apothecary in colonial America at any time during the eighteenth century. They all published for their prospective customers lengthy lists of items just imported, and the lists bear a marked resemblance from place to place and from time to time.

WILLIAMSBURG, *August* 31, 1769.

Just imported in the EXPERIMENT, *Capt.* HAMLIN,

A FRESH and compleat assortment of DRUGS and MEDICINES, chymical and galenical, which will be SOLD at a very low advance for READY CASH, and are as follows:

Crude antimony, æther, verdigrease, Barbados, hepatick, and succotrine aloes, common and rock alum, ambergrise, compound waters of all kinds, quicksilver, balsams of capivi, Peru, amber, and Tolu, Canadian balsam, Armenian bole, borax, calomel crude and prepared, camphor, canella alba, cantharides, cloves, Indian pink; greatly celebrated for destroying worms in children, Russian and Hudson's Bay castors, common and lunar caustick, cinnabar of antimony, native and fictitious cinnabar, potash, cochineal, colcothar, vitriol, colocynth, confectio cardiaca, conserves of hips, sloes, and sorrel roses, wormwood and orange peel, Jesuits bark, cinnamon, cascarilla, cremor tartar, English and Spanish saffron, elaterium, plaisters and electuaries of all kinds, essence of lemons, burgamot and ambergrease, single and double camomile flowers, flower of brimstone, balaustines, senna, galls, grains of paradise, gums of all kinds, pearl barley, isinglass, Irish slate, litharge, common and flakey manna, sweet mercury, calcined mercury, corrosive sublimate, red precipitate, musk, chymical oils, opium, long pepper, ipecacuanha, jalap, gentian, licorice, contrayerva, calamus aromaticus, china and sarsaparilla, best Turkey and India rhubarb, valerian, sago, alkaline, neutral, and volatile salts, saloop, seeds of anise, carraway, coriander, wild carrot, fennel and fennugreek, lesser cardamoms, staves acre, spermaceti, spirits of hartshorn, lavender, sal volatile, and sal ammoniac, nitre, mineral acids, dulcified spirits of salt, vitriol, and sal ammoniac, Spanish licorice, tartar emetic, vermacelli, white, blue, and green vitriols, extract of hemlock, glass of antimony, meadow, saffron, and mezereon roots, common and Nesbitt's clyster pipes, gold and silver leaf, Dutch metal, gallipots and vials, Anderson's, Hooper's, and Lockyer's pills, Turlington's balsam, Hill's pectoral balsam of honey, Bateman's drops, Squire's, Daffy's, and Bostock's elixirs, Freeman's and Godfrey's cordials, British oil, eau de luce, Dr. James's fever powder, court plaister, best lavender and Hungary waters, &c. &c.

The subscriber intends opening shop at the BRICK HOUSE, opposite the Coffee-House, when he gets his utensils fixed, which will be in a fortnight at furthest; and as this is his first importation, every thing may be depended upon as entirely fresh, and bought of one of the best hands in *London*. Those who please to favour him with their orders, may depend on having them immediately dispatched, and every thing put up in the best manner, by

Their most obedient humble servant,
JOHN MINSON GALT.

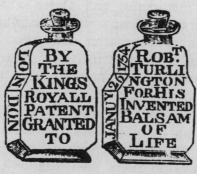

Turlington's Balsam of Life *bottles a: pictured in a brochure dated 1755-1757, preserved in the Pennsylvania Historical Society, Philadelphia, Pa. According to Turlington, the bottle was adopted in 1754 "to prevent the villainy of some persons who, buying up my empty bottles, have basely and wickedly put therein a vile spurious counterfeit sort."*

An apt example is the advertisement placed in the *Virginia Gazette* of September 21, 1769, by John Minson Galt at the outset of his long career (facing page).

Analysis of the Galt or any other advertisement of the time shows that the contents of a colonial apothecary shop fell into five categories: plant materials, animal extracts, metals and metallic derivatives, medical equipment, and prepared elixirs, pills, and the like.

Among the most popular of the prepared medicines— judging from the many advertisements of Dr. John Minson Galt in the years 1772–1774—were Dr. Keyser's celebrated anti-venereal pills. These were backed by testimonials of two English and three French dukes, and Galt published lengthy accounts avowing that "the Patient is most effectually cured without any Inconvenience to himself, or being exposed to the Shame and Confusion of his Disaster being known to the nicest Observer."

Not only were they supposed to cure syphilis, but "the happy effects of *Keyser's* pills have often been proved in white Swellings, asthmas, Suppressions of the Urine, in the Palsy, Apoplexies, Sciaticks, in the Green Sickness, and more especially in the Yaws."

"Mrs. Rednapp's red fit drops" were among Dr. Pasteur's

favorite patent medicines, and Daffy's, Stoughton's, and Bateman's elixirs or drops were distributed not only by most colonial apothecaries but also by the keepers of general stores, ship captains, and others. In 1771 no fewer than nineteen packaged English medicines were offered for sale at the Post Office in Williamsburg!

The formulas for some of these, consisting of twenty or more separate ingredients, were printed in the principal pharmacopoeias and were commonly made up by doctors and apothecaries for their own use and for sale. Dr. Pasteur and Dr. James Carter both ordered quantities of empty bottles for Stoughton's and Daffy's compounds.

Dependence on imported patent medicines was a development that several observers deplored. Dr. Schoepf, for instance, thought American physicians should patriotically discontinue "making use almost wholly of foreign medicines, with which in large measure they might easily dispense, if they were willing to give their attention to home-products, informing themselves more exactly of the properties and uses of the stock of domestic medicines already known."

Jefferson in his *Notes on the State of Virginia* had listed twenty-one medicinal plants native to the state, and others before him had commented on the abundance of simple remedies afforded by the woods and marshes of tidewater Virginia. Indeed, it appears that colonial medical men in the seventeenth century had gathered the largest part of their own medicines close at hand, and that the growing importation of patent mixtures was matched by an increasing export of native drugs.

By the middle of the eighteenth century considerable quantities of at least eight medicinal plants were being shipped to England from Virginia, among them ipecacuanha, sassafras, balsam of Tolu, ginseng, and snakeroot. The last two formed the bulk of the export; of them more in a moment.

However, if there were in colonial towns "some apothe-

POLYGALA *Virginiana folijs oblongis floribus in thyrſs candidis radice, Alexipharmica* MILLER

PRESENTEM OSTENDIT QUÆLIBET HERBA DEUM

Seneca
Rattle-Snake Root

Seneca rattlesnake root or Polygala Virginiana *was a mainstay of medical treatment in eighteenth-century Virginia. The original source of this drawing has not been identified.*

caries shops wainscotted or papered with advertisements, recommending quack medicines," a large number of rural practitioners preferred to make up their remedies. "I do not apply to the Apothecaries Shops for my Means," said the advertisement of one such, "I compact my own medicines myself. The produce of *Virginia* Earth, with a few trifles besides, supports my Body, ... and many others besides, without bleeding, sweating, physicking, or Bitters."

Whether used from conviction that such means were better, or because the imported medicines were too expensive, the result was the same: such mild cures were less likely to interfere with the healing course of nature than did the complex, often drastic, and sometimes revolting compounds of the leading English physicians.

From inventories of the estates of deceased apothecaries as well as from their newspaper advertisements comes evidence as to the equipment they kept and used in their shops. The remarkable thing is to see how little the essential items have changed over the course of the centuries—alike before and since the colonial era.

The mortar and pestle, traditional symbol of the apothecary's calling and often used as the sign of his shop, was to be found in Williamsburg shops in many sizes and materials. The largest recorded was a bell-metal mortar and iron pestle belonging to Dr. Thomas Wharton and weighing 168 pounds. Wharton also owned a large marble mortar and pestle, two small ones of marble, and a "Porphrey Stone & Muller." Later in the century, as the medical profession learned that toxic quantities of metal dust could come from the use of metal mortars, ceramic and glass became widely used.

Glass and ceramic containers by the hundreds were also used to store simple ingredients and compounds for sale. Dr. Pasteur at one time, for instance, ordered 246 white glass vials ranging in capacity from two drams to twelve ounces. Dr. Alexander Middleton, whose tory sympathies cost him his Williamsburg shop and contents during the Revolution, listed more than fifty dozen bottles, from one ounce size to two gallons, along with dozens of pill pots, ointment pots, and syrup pots. Glass seems to have been the most common type of container, with earthenware "gallipots" probably second.

Among the articles with which the Williamsburg shop is furnished are a number that belonged to the first Dr. Galt that have been obtained from his descendants or generously loaned by them to Colonial Williamsburg. The largest is the secretary-bookcase that stands in the back office, the most numerous are the scores of glass bottles and cardboard pillboxes that cluster on one section of the shelves, and perhaps the most interesting are his diplomas in anatomy, surgery, and midwifery that hang on the wall. Vying with the last named is the account book displaying a charge of 7 shillings against Patrick Henry—but no entry to show that the bill was ever paid.

It would require more space than is here available to describe, or even to list, all the articles in the shop today, and to identify all the drugs, herbs, powders, and compounds that would have been contained in the numerous bottles, jars, boxes, and drawers of the shop. The quantity and variety, however, may be taken as typical of a well provided apothecary shop of colonial America.

One should note in particular the surgical instruments in their velvet-lined cases. These have been collected from various sources—including one case of lancets and a set of scales from the Galt family—and are of the period. Dr. Alexander Middleton claimed to have been deprived in the Revolution of instruments for amputating, trepanning, lithotomy, cupping, couching, dissecting, dentistry, and midwifery. The estate of Dr. Kenneth McKenzie of Williamsburg inventoried three sets of instruments for amputating, trepanning, and lithotomy.

The McKenzie inventory also listed the medical books in Dr. McKenzie's library. There were more than seventy titles, of which all but a few were medical treatises, some of them in several volumes. Among them were listed *James' Dispensatory* and *Shaw's Dispensatory*. These, along with *Bate's Dispensatory* and the *London Dispensatory* were among the most widely read, owned, and used books in the colony, and not alone by doctors or apothecaries. One or more was almost certain to be in the library of every planter of tidewater Virginia, a kind of "What to do till the Doctor comes" manual for the home treatment of the planter himself, his wife and children, his relatives and neighbors, and his slaves. These dispensatories avoided the need or cost of a doctor's services unless the trouble was so serious as to need "expert" attention.

This was by no means such an unwise system as at first glance may appear. After all, the doctor would probably dose with the same medicines from the same dispensatory, and with the same result. And while quacks were plentiful, well-trained physicians were extremely scarce, especially in rural areas where pay was sure to be slow and skimpy.

In view of the general state of medical knowledge and practice throughout the eighteenth century—bleeding being always a foremost treatment of numerous ailments—it seems likely that the liberal use of native herbs, being for the most part harmless, was probably the safest and most effective course of medication. Surely human and animal excreta, mashed-up insects, and the like, which were not uncommon in London prescriptions, could not have been more curative than rattlesnake root and ginseng, whose praises were sung by the famous William Byrd II:

> The Earth has never produced any vegetable so friendly to man as Ginseng. Nor do I say this at Random, or by the strength of my Faith, but by my own Experience. I have found it very cordial and reviving after great Fatigue, it warms the Blood, frisks the Spirits strengthens the Stomach and comforts the Bowels exceedingly. All this it performs

with out any of those naughty Effects that might make men too troublesome and impertinent to their poor Wives.

Then as for the Rattlesnake Root the Reputation of it encreases every day. The Tincture of it has done Wonders in the Gout.... By its purging, its deuretick, and diaphoretick Qualities it is of great use in the Dropsy ... of great Efficacy in Pleuretick Feaver . . . [and] a Specifick against worms. . . .

For the Bite of a mad Dog, . . . it may perhaps be as Sure a Remedy; as for the Bite of a Rattlesnake.

A List of Williamsburg Apothecaries

This list includes only those medical practitioners of eighteenth-century Williamsburg who operated apothecary shops. It does not include physicians who may have made up and dispensed their own prescriptions but did not operate a shop.

Andrew Anderson (1768–1771)
> Anderson studied medicine in England after serving an apprenticeship with Dr. James Carter. Anderson returned to Williamsburg in 1768 and formed a partnership with Dr. Carter and they purchased the shop of William Biers. Anderson moved to New Kent County in 1771 and in 1774 married Betsey Burnet, "an agreeable young Lady, with a handsome Fortune."

Robert Anderson (1764)
> Anderson advertised his apothecary shop in Williamsburg in 1764.

William Biers (1765–1768)
> Biers operated a druggist shop in Williamsburg from about 1765 to 1768 when he sold his business to Dr. Carter and Dr. Anderson. In 1769 Biers announced his intention to leave the colony.

James Carter (1751–1779)

Dr. Carter opened his apothecary shop, "the Unicorn's Horn," in Williamsburg in 1751 and operated it until 1779 when he sold it to his brother William Carter. James continued to practice medicine in Williamsburg until his death in 1794.

William Carter, (1773–1784)

In 1771 William Carter established his medical practice in Gloucester County. In 1773 he came to Williamsburg and formed a partnership with his brother James. Six years later he purchased his brother's share of "the Unicorn's Horn," and in 1784 he moved to Richmond where he opened another apothecary shop.

Robert Davidson (1737–1739)

Dr. Davidson, mayor of Williamsburg, operated a druggist shop in partnership with Thomas Goodwin from 1737 to 1739 when Davidson died.

John Minson Galt (1769–1808)

After studying medicine in England, Galt opened his apothecary shop in 1769. From 1775 until 1778 he operated a shop in partnership with Dr. William Pasteur. In 1795 Galt was appointed visiting physician to the hospital for the insane and in 1799 he was appointed a member of the court of directors for the hospital.

George Gilmer, Sr. (1731–1757)

A graduate of the University of Edinburgh, Dr. Gilmer established an apothecary shop in Williamsburg in 1731. He operated the shop in connection with a successful medical practice until his death in 1757.

George Gilmer, Jr. (1766–1771)

After completing his medical studies in England, Gilmer returned to Williamsburg in 1766 and

opened his apothecary shop. In 1771 he moved
to Charlottesville and established a successful
practice.

Thomas Goodwin (1735–1739)

Goodwin owned a druggist shop in Williamsburg
and apparently did not engage in a medical
practice. From 1737 to 1739 he conducted the
shop in partnership with Dr. Robert Davidson.

Peter Hay (1744–1766)

Dr. Hay conducted an apothecary shop in Williamsburg from 1744 until his death in 1766
when he was described as "one of our most
eminent physicians."

Kenneth McKenzie (1732–1755)

Dr. McKenzie owned an apothecary shop in
Williamsburg from 1732 until his death in 1755.

Alexander Middleton (1776)

Dr. Middleton operated an apothecary shop in
Williamsburg in 1776. Middleton, a tory, was
forced to leave Virginia during the Revolutionary
War.

Robert Nicolson (1779–1783)

Dr. Nicolson served his apprenticeship with
Dr. Pasteur and then studied medicine in England.
He returned to Williamsburg in 1779 and opened
his apothecary shop. After the Revolutionary
War he moved his shop to Yorktown where he
practiced medicine until his death in 1798.

William Pasteur (1757–1791)

After the completion of his apprenticeship with
Dr. George Gilmer, Sr., Pasteur studied in England for about a year. He returned to Williamsburg in 1757 and established an apothecary shop.
From 1775 to 1778 he operated the shop in
partnership with John Minson Galt.

George Pitt (1744–1768)

Dr. Pitt, born in 1724 in England and "bred a Surgeon," established his apothecary shop in Williamsburg in 1744 at the "Sign of the Rhinoceros." In 1768 he closed his shop and returned to England. He later came back to Virginia but no longer engaged in medicine or pharmacy. In 1776 Pitt, a tory, left Virginia again. He died later that year in England.

Thomas Wharton (1735–1746)

Wharton arrived in Virginia about 1703 as an indentured servant to Dr. Richard Wright. By 1735 Wharton had established an apothecary shop in Williamsburg, which he operated until his death in 1746. He left his drugs, medicines, and shop utensils to Dr. McKenzie.

Suggestions for Further Reading

Whitfield J. Bell, Jr., *The Colonial Physician & Other Essays*. New York: Science History Publications, 1975.

———, "Medical Practice in Colonial America," in *Symposium on Colonial Medicine*. Williamsburg: Jamestown-Williamsburg-Yorktown Celebration Commission and the Virginia 350th Anniversary Commission, 1957.

John B. Blake, *Public Health in the Town of Boston, 1630–1822*. Cambridge, Mass.: Harvard University Press, 1959.

Wyndham B. Blanton, *Medicine in Virginia in the Eighteenth Century*. Richmond: Garrett and Massie, 1931.

———, *Medicine in Virginia in the Seventeenth Century*. Richmond: William Byrd Press, 1930.

John Duffy, *A History of Public Health in New York City, 1625–1866*. New York: Russell Sage Foundation, 1968.

Harold B. Gill, Jr., *The Apothecary in Colonial Virginia*. Williamsburg: Colonial Williamsburg Foundation, 1972.

George B. Griffenhagen, *Drug Supplies in the American Revolution*. Washington, D. C.: Contributions from the Museum of History and Technology, Bulletin No. 225, 1961.

———, *Tools of the Apothecary*. Washington, D. C.: American Pharmaceutical Association, 1957.

Patrick Henderson, "Smallpox and Patriotism: The Norfolk Riots, 1768–1769." *Virginia Magazine of History and Biography,* LXXIII (October 1965), pp. 413–424.

Thomas P. Hughes, *Medicine in Virginia, 1607–1699*. Williamsburg: Virginia 350th Anniversary Celebration Corporation, 1957.

Thomas Jefferson, *Notes on the State of Virginia,* ed. William Peden. Chapel Hill: University of North Carolina Press, 1955.

Edward Kremers and George Urdang, *History of Pharmacy: A Guide and a Survey.* Philadelphia: J. B. Lippincott Co., 1951.

Geoffrey Marks and William K. Beatty, "The Virginia Colony," in *The Story of Medicine in America.* New York: Charles Scribner's Sons, 1973.

Benjamin Rush, *The Autobiography of Benjamin Rush,* ed. George W. Corner. Princeton: Princeton University Press, 1948.

Richard Harrison Shryock, *Medicine and Society in America: 1660–1860.* New York: New York University Press, 1960.

C. J. S. Thompson, *The Mystery and Art of the Apothecary.* Philadelphia: J. B. Lippincott Co., 1929.

Surry Wood, *The Old Apothecary Shop.* Watkins Glen, N.Y.: Century House, 1956.

The Apothecary in Eighteenth-Century Williamsburg was first published in 1965 and previously reprinted in 1968, 1970, 1973, 1978, 1982, 1984, 1985, 1986, 1987, 1988, 1990, 1991, 1993, 1995, 1997, 1998, and 2000. Written by Thomas K. Ford, late editor of Colonial Williamsburg publications, it is based largely on a monograph by Harold B. Gill, Jr. That study has been published as *The Apothecary in Colonial Virginia* (Williamsburg, Virginia, 1972).

ISBN 0-910412-16-2